CW00669816

Oliver Kilbourn

My Life as a Pitman

ASHINGTON GROUP TRUSTEES
2008

For Margaret ('Peggy') Kilbourn 1914–2006

First published 1992 by Mid Northumberland Arts Group 1992
Second edition by Ashington Group Trustees 2008
Woodhorn Colliery Museum · Ashington NE63 9YS

ISBN 978 0 9554138 1 0

Introduction © William Feaver 2008
Illustrations © Ashington Group Trustees 2008

All rights reserved. No part of this publication may be reproduced, stored in a retrieval system, or transmitted, in any form or by any means, without the prior permission in writing of the Ashington Group Trustees, or as expressly permitted by law, or under terms agreed with the appropriate reprographic rights organisation.

Designed and typeset in Arnhem by Dalrymple
Printed in Northern Ireland by Nicholson & Bass

Illustrated on front cover: *The artist, again aged 14, pulling the hogger [hose] to couple it to the main compressed air pipe*
Frontispiece: *Hewing*

Funding towards this edition has been provided through the generosity of the Live Theatre, Newcastle upon Tyne who donated the proceeds of a performance on 28 October 2007 of Lee Hall's play, *The Pitmen Painters*.

Oliver Kilbourn (1904 – 1993) was one of the founder members of the Ashington Group. The principal collection of the Group's work is permanently on display in Woodhorn Colliery Museum. A separate sequence of paintings by Oliver, *My Life as a Pitman*, is also on show at the Museum; and this catalogue gives details of those paintings.

Foreword to the First Edition

I was born at Ashington in 1904, the son of a pitman. I went to an elementary school and left in Standard 7. I was 13 on Friday 6 October 1917 and started work at Ashington Colliery the following Monday.

At 14 years of age I started as a pom pom boy on the compressed air coal-cutting machines. We raked out the scufflings, the tiny bits of coal duff that were cut by the machine and cast them aside. I stayed on this job until I was over 16 when I became a putter lad for about seven years, pulling empty tubs to the coal-face and returning with full ones. The Duke Pit at Ashington was then closed down, so I moved to Ellington Colliery, a few miles away and stayed there for the rest of my working life. I became a coal-face drawer there when I was 24.

During the war years I was put on to salvage drawing to help in an effort to save as much material as possible – girders, pit props, all kinds of timber. I carried on with that until about three years before I retired [in 1968] when I took a lighter job as a wasteman, repairing and looking after airways and keeping them in good order.

So much for my working life, now for what I did between shifts. While I was still a junior, Ashington Colliery started their Welfare Scheme, one of the first in the country. I played football for the Bothal Pit in their Junior League, and in my early teens I went to a tutorial class run by the Ashington Miners' Union. This gave me a love of knowledge that has stayed with me ever since.

I continued with Workers' Educational Association classes, and in 1934 they started an eight-year course in art appreciation. This was the foundation of the Ashington Group of Painters, and art has been my main interest in my life since then.

OLIVER KILBOURN, 1992

An Introduction to Oliver Kilbourn

WILLIAM FEAVER

'After I retired I had quite a lot of time on my hands and I thought it wouldn't be any harm if I painted something I really knew about; and so I did *My Life as a Pitman'*.

This takes Oliver Kilbourn back over seventy years, to the day he was set out on his first job: raking out a Siskel pom pom in the west cross cuts, Bothal High Main seam, Ashington Colliery. He sees his fourteen-year-old self, remote now as though stuck at the far end of a peepshow, clearing a fresh cut in the coal-face, dragging a hogger, or compressed-air hose, along to the main supply pipe, and then, on his own, fastening full tubs on to the trot (endless rope) that led out to the shaft and brought back empties.

'I wouldn't say I had a driving ambition to get down the pit, I just stayed down there fifty years – a working life. After a lot of groaning and grumbling you took a pride in your job, you know. It's a very skilful job.'

Artists have two standard ways of portraying miners. Either as stocky, heroic toilers or as blackened hulks. They are shown at work, forever hacking away at gleaming walls of coal or crammed into the lift-cage poised for the descent. What passes for underground realism is generally over-blown romance, all grovel and backstrain.

Look at the way Oliver Kilbourn demonstrates the process of filling a tub. There are three drawings of the one operation. 'Why do three? It was to show that it wasn't just a simple action. That the putter lad had to get the tub in, turn it round and then shove it in from behind -like a matador with a bull: twist and let it go by. Awkward to do, but graceful, like a dance step 123. Quite unique I think.' The stages of drilling a shot, firing it, hewing and eventually, shifting the conveyor belt on to a new track and filling off a face are all made clear, illustrated not because they offer scope for the artist to show off his figure-drawing and light effects, but because he believes they need to be seen.

The idea behind this belief dates back more than fifty years, to 1934 when the Ashington Group began. It was originally a WEA class which, having exhausted 'Evolution' as a topic, decided to take up art for a change. A tutor was sent from Newcastle, a lecturer at King's College named Robert Lyon, and he soon decided that the only way

Stonemen setting arch girders

After the caunch is redd the stonemen strengthen the roof by setting arch girders. This all applies to the period before the modern mechanisation of collieries, which lasted well into the 1950s. CAT.37

to inculcate principles of art appreciation was to get the men to tryout techniques for themselves. As self-consciousness wore off, the class became increasingly pre-occupied with painting subjects drawn from immediate experience:

Ashington scenes, everyday incidents. They began exhibiting, gained recognition, and were taken up by Mass-Observation, the Thirties socialdocumentation movement. Eventually they found themselves to be the only genuine, lasting group of working-men painters to survive the fashion for such bodies at that time.

The members stayed together in strength for about ten years and the Group survived as a thoroughly independent body through to the eighties. Meetings were held on Monday nights in an old army hut next to the Hirst Industrial Club in the middle of Ashington.

The Ashington Group was conceived as an experiment in 'seeing by doing'. It flourished as a clubby yet self-critical body. Paintings were not done to be sold or even displayed at home. They were objects for discussion, to be argued over, evaluated not so much in aesthetic terms as true-to-life ones. The whole emphasis, Oliver remembers, was 'Start painting: it's as simple as that. The picture that nobody else has painted before, copied off nobody. Something that you feel strongly about.' They painted scenes below ground, views of the streets and fields and coast round Ashington, pictures of leek beds, whippet training, domestic routines with child-rearing, mat-making, going on-shift, Sunday dinner. Some of them developed specialities. Jimmy Floyd for instance delighted in allotment life. Harry Wilson recorded social wrongs, believing that to paint open drains was in itself a form of protest.

The Galloway Field at Ashington Colliery
Young ponies sporting before being broken-in (trained) and sent underground CAT.6

Calling the weigh
This was one of the first jobs given to young boys before they went down below. The boy called out the number on the filler's token to the weighman (who was employed by the coal company) who recorded the weight of coal shown on his weighing-machine and credited it to the filler concerned. The other man in the cabin is the check-weighman who was employed by the Miners' Union to ensure that the fillers' weights were correctly recorded. He also kept a fatherly eye on the boys. CAT.5

8

Lowse – end of shift
Ponies at the stable going through the wash-pond in the 1920s. Lowse is a dialect form of loose – to release, free from bonds. CAT.24

Deputy's kist [chest or office]
Oncoming shift of conveyor fillers reporting to the deputy after walking inbye. CAT.22

The Kilbourn paintings in the Group archive also housed in Woodhorn Colliery Museum were, from the very beginning, distinguishable, from all the rest. Not on the grounds of quality or subject matter but in style and in attitude. Whereas Jimmy Floyd was a fine naive, Harry Wilson a painstaking striver, Fred Laidler a craftsman intent on honouring his tools and materials, Oliver Kilbourn has always revealed himself to be the one with what can only be described as artistic instincts. By which I mean he has an observant attitude, seeing things as an interpreter rather than as a straightforward participant, and he works with his idols – Hogarth, Bewick and Turner – in mind. In doing so he creates immense difficulties for himself, makes it impossible to plead innocence. His passion for painting has complicated his reactions. His pit ponies rub up against Stubbs' horses.

'I can handle the medium with more fluency than I could when I first started', he says, adding with vital though inhibiting self-awareness: 'That may be a drawback.' Proficiency in Art Group terms, with a subject a week to consider and work out, is not enough when it comes to acting solo.

At the same time, Oliver does have his subject matter. Others may polish their skills, perfect their technique, while trying to think of something to say. He has the memories to draw on, a sense of 'the passion of the past', an urge to recall. And, like the topographers who accompanied Cook to the South Seas, he finds himself a pretty well unique, expert witness. Others may generalise about working conditions underground. He knows them. Thousands of other pitmen share his experiences: he is one of the very few who have proved capable of expressing them.

My Life as a Pitman is to some extent a resume of all the past themes in his work. Some years ago he did a series of pen and ink drawings of a day in the life of a young lad which anticipates the present cycle. He showed the mother rousing him to go on-shift, the streets of Ashington at 2am, the fear of being stranded alone in the dark. 'It used to be creepy in the pit. You could hear little bits of things going on. Timber creaking, bits of stone dropping here and there. Until you got used to it you were frightened: you didn't know what was really happening. I mean, a lad of fourteen years old, you were rather scared to go by yourself anywhere. You liked to get where other people were working.'

Years later, Oliver had advanced through the jobs to become a salvage drawer, the most skilled occupation underground. 'A drawer had to known when the goaf [waste working] was safe. You could hear the little rumbles at first and they'd turn to cracks and then they'd be like sort of hard rents and you'd have to be very careful and set more timbers. Also sometimes you would just see a little bit of dust fallen from the roof and

Geton! How-way!! SANDY!!!

Pulling out the full tub. CAT.16

then a little bit of stone broken, then a bit more then a bigger bit, and you'd know it was time to get some extra supports in – props about 21/2 or 3 foot, about an inch less than required – and within a minute of setting them they would be pinched between roof and floor.'

In his pictures of timber-setting and drawing procedures, of Stonemen redding mothergate caunch, Oliver shows his delight in the unison of a gang of men, testing, shifting, securing. Here the labour takes on a special urgency. It's a struggle for safety and survival. Equally telling is the image of the filler shovelling coal into a tub by candlelight, his jacket hung neatly on a prop, the timbered perspective receding into pitch darkness. The pitman's existence, he emphasises, alternates between close comradeship and hours of utter solitude.

'You were isolated you know, in a place hundreds of yards from anybody else except the putter lad going in every now and again, and the deputy who, by law, had to make at least two inspections per shift. If there was any dangerous stone hanging or gas or anything like that, he would say, "Be careful of that right-hand corner there, I don't like the look of that stone: I'd get a prop in and a plank." But when he went away we'd keep filling those tubs and probably not bother about it. Sometimes though you were unfortunate and it maybe came down and lamed you or something. That was often happening.

'Some seams here were just two feet, some eighteen inches and there was one called the two-yard seam which seemed paradise compared with the two-foot seam. 'You were on your knees and sometimes lying on your back or sideways that sort of thing and you were glad to get your legs stretched a bit so you might walk out to the main gateway. Then you'd go in again. On the whole, the getting of coal was so intense you hadn't much time to think about other things really during your shift. In the days when you just had candles and whatnot it was very, very gloomy.'

One painting in the series stands out from the general shadowiness. It shows the great field at Ashington Colliery where young Galloway ponies were free to run before the time came for them to be broken in and sent underground. 'It was a bit of a shame that these ponies, very innocent of the jobs they were to come to below were sporting about and enjoying life to the full. Down the pit they were held to the hard and fast rule. And they never came up, that was the tragedy of it.'

The putter lads harnessing up, stealing rides on the ponies, chivvying them along ('Come now Sandy, that's right now. Whoa! Hold on!'), sending them floundering through the washpond at the end of the shift, these scenes, the focus of the early stages of the series, may seem to invite sentimental responses. But what emerges is that, whereas the green fields are idealised to the point of being pretty-pretty, the under-world of tunnels, burrows and timbered mazes is matter of fact.

It is impossible to say exactly when Oliver began to harbour notions about painting his life. Certainly it was before the Ashington Group began. 'I took a great desire to express myself as an artist, not with any thought of gain or anything like that. I couldn't express myself so well in words but I found that I could express my feelings and what I wanted to get over in drawing and painting.'

He was born in Chestnut Street, Ashington in 1904. 'My home life was quite good really. I was brought up strictly as a Wesleyan – had to go to Chapel and Sunday School. Our life was more or less centred on that and disciplined to a very high degree. I left school from Standard 7, able to read and write, I'll say that for it. I remember one of the first books I read was, *The Last of the Mohicans* by Fenimore Cooper.

'Art was very scanty though. The art training was just a few flowers and bits of objects put on a table. Pencil and pastel only: no paint or anything like that. It wasn't taken too seriously. But I had an interest in art, I've been painting and drawing ever since I can remember. At home we had these cement floors and long before I went to school I was always drawing on them with chalks. My mother was very fond of them and she didn't rub them out until they got to be too much. She'd lay clicky mats on them and I'd come in, pull the rug back and start where I'd left off.'

His father took him in to Newcastle once or twice to see the pictures in the Laing Art Gallery. 'Unfortunately, when I was about eleven, my father had an accident in the pit and damaged his back. He was brought home on a flat cart and never worked again. There was just a little bit of compensation, not much like, but it helped. Once I'd left school I became the breadwinner more or less, maintaining the whole family on 14 shillings a week till my sisters got jobs. One went into service, two worked in shops.'

My Life as a Pitman isn't a saga of regrets and deprivations. It represents accomplishments, tasks, concerns. There are implicit fears, reminders all along that conditions have changed, that circumstances have changed even more. Kilbourn's life is now a history; as much a history as the Bayeux Tapestry. It flows from one picture to the next, this definitive account of Ashington underground.

Catalogue of Paintings by Oliver Kilbourn at Woodhorn Colliery Museum

NOTES ON THE LISTINGS

All the paintings are in acrylic on watercolour paper. All measurements are in centimetres: height × width.

The paintings in this catalogue were produced in the mid-1970s.

FURTHER READING

William Feaver, *Pitmen Painters: The Ashington Group, 1934–1984,* Ashington and Manchester, 1993

Catalogue of the Ashington Group, Ashington, 2006.

1 *The artist at the age of 14 raking out on the pom poms*

Pom pom was the nickname for the Siskel coal-cutter, one of the earliest coalcutting machines. It is pictured here in the west cross cuts, Bothal High Main Seam, Ashington Colliery.

50.5 × 75.6 CM
ASH MM 1989/18.1

2 *The artist, again aged 14, pulling the hogger [hose] to couple it to the main compressed air pipe*

The pom pom has been set up for cutting, and runs on compressed-air.

49.6 × 75.6 CM
ASH MM 1989/18.2

3 *Trotting*

Boy sending full tubs outbye (the route to the shaft bottom) by hanging them on to an endless rope called the trot. The trot is a system of double haulage way called the rolleyway which takes the full tubs of coal to the shaft and the empty tubs inbye to the flat. The flat is usually at the end of the rolleyway where the double haulageway system converges into a single way leading to the working area called the whole.

55 × 75.6 CM
ASH MM 1989/18.3

4 *Knocking off the fork*

The fork or ham bone is a clip used to attach tubs to the endless rope. Knocking off the fork releases the set of full tubs on a landing outbye.

55 × 75.7 CM
ASH MM 1989/18.4

5 *Calling the weigh*

This was one of the first jobs given to young boys before they went down below. The boy called out the number on the filler's token to the weighman (who was employed by the coal company) who recorded the weight of coal shown on his weighing-machine and credited it to the filler concerned. The other man in the cabin is the check-weighman who was employed by the Miners' Union to ensure that the fillers' weights were correctly recorded. He also kept a fatherly eye on the boys.

55.6 × 75.G CM
ASH MM 1989/18.5

6 *The Galloway Field at Ashington Colliery*

Young ponies sporting before being broken-in (trained) and sent underground

55 CM × 75.2 CM
ASH MM 1989/18.6

7 *Putters on the heap collecting their tokens*

This is at the beginning of a shift. The pithead was known as the heap, and the putters, like the fillers, had to hang a token inside each full tub that they put (pulled out from the filler to the flat). The fillers were paid by the tonnage but the putters were paid by the score (20) of tubs.

55 × 75.2 CM
ASH MM 1989/18.7

8 Putters at the beginning of their shift leaving the stables

The putters are ready to go inbye with their Galloways (ponies). Putters were usually aged from 16 to about 23 and their job was to take the empry tubs into the coal fillers' place and pull out the full tubs to the flat and this was considered the starting point of coal-face work before progressing to the more skilled jobs at the face.

55 × 75.2 CM
ASH MM 1989/18.8

9 Goinginbye

Putters riding ponies. This was forbidden but was often done by the boys.

43 CM × 75.4 CM
ASH MM 1989/18.9

10 Yoking-up at the deputy's kist

Ponies are brought from the stables just wearing harness. The limmers are attached to the harness at the deputy's kist (chest). The limmers are similar to cart shafts except that they are not permanently attached to the tubs.

55.4 CM × 75.4 CM
ASH MM 1989/18.10

11 Gannin in chum

A chum is an empty tub.

55 × 75.5 CM
ASH MM 1989/18.11

12 Leaving the chummin

Leaving the chummin at the end of the bord to go'and pull out the full one taken from the filler.

50 × 75.2 CM
ASH MM 1989/18.12

13 Filler filling tub I

54 × 73.8 CM
ASH MM 1989/18.13

14 Filler filling tub II

53.7 CM × 74 CM
ASH MM 1989/18.14

15 Filler filling tub III

54 × 74 CM
ASH MM 1989/18.15

16 Geton! How-way!! SANDY!!!

Pulling out the full tub.

49.7 × 75.5 CM
ASH MM 1989/18.16

17 Pulling the full tub from the filler

54 × 74 CM
ASH MM 1989/18.17

18 Riding the limmers through a swalley

A swalley is a dip in the roadway which is often full of water. The putter is taking a full tub to the flat.

50 × 75 CM
ASH MM 1989/18.18

19 Off the way

Putter lifting the tub back on to the rails.

50 × 75.7 CM
ASH MM 1989/18.19

20 Putters on the flat

The flat is where the putters exchange their full tubs for empties.

53.7 × 75.2 CM
ASH MM 1989/18.20

21 'Marker there' [Mark it there]

The deputy is sighting a direction so the roadway can be driven straight. A lowe is dialect for 'light'. The deputy uses two plumb-lines and aligns them with a light at the coal-face.

54 × 75.5 CM
ASH MM 1989/18.21

22 Lowse – end of shift

Ponies at the stable going through the washpond in the 1920s. Lowse is a dialect form of loose – to release, free from bonds.

53.5 × 75.2 CM
ASH MM 1989/18.22

23 Washing ponies in the 1960s

54 × 75.2 CM
ASH MM 1989/18.23